Murder the Foundation Stone

Elizabeth Hourston

With illustration by Leila Thomson
and calligraphy by Connie Hogarth

ISBN 0 9512281 0 2

Printed in Great Britain by
The Kirkwall Press,
Kirkwall,
Orkney.

For Hetty, George and Douglas.

HISTORICAL BACKGROUND

In the twelfth century two Viking jarls, Magnus Erlendsson and Haakon Paulsson, ruled the earldom of Orkney. Their power sharing presented difficulties and in April, 1117, they agreed to meet on the isle of Egilsay with a specified number of men and ships to settle their differences. Haakon betrayed the tryst, overpowered Magnus and had him murdered.

After Haakon's death, the King of Norway granted to Rognvald, Magnus' nephew, his murdered uncle's half of the earldom. Haakon's heir, Paul, was loathe to surrender any of his territory and Rognvald, with the aid of his father, Kol, set about gaining his inheritance by force. Rognvald vowed that, if he was successful, he would build a cathedral to the memory of his murdered uncle, Magnus.

By this time, Magnus was widely regarded as a martyr, and reports were rife of miraculous happenings worked at his grave. Bishop William the Old, mindful no doubt of the relationship between Church and State, was slow to accept such claims, but eventually was persuaded to sanctify Magnus and lend his support to Rognvald.

Kol employed various stratagems in his attack on Orkney, launching a false offensive from Shetland, sabotaging the warning beacon on the Fair Isle and choosing a wind which would help him, but hinder Earl Paul. Eventually Rognvald landed on Westray and a truce was arranged between the rival earls by Bishop William.

In the meantime, however, Sweyn Asleifsson, a Viking of the old mould, had been taunted by, and had murdered

Paul's man, Sweyn Breastrope. He was immediately exiled and Bishop William helped him to escape to the Western Isles. Sweyn, however, was intent on revenging himself on Paul for his exile and on repaying his debt to William. He therefore returned to Orkney, came on Earl Paul hunting otter in Rousay and abducted him, killing his men and thus leaving the way clear for Rognvald to become sole earl of the islands. Some time later, however, Sweyn, who was always alert for his own advancement, supported the claim of Paul's nephew, Harald, to half the earldom. Rognvald, wisely, instead of opposing this move, adopted Harald as his foster son, thus avoiding conflict.

In 1137 Rognvald set about redeeming his pledge. Kol was the chief architect of the cathedral and it is believed that the masons who built St. Magnus may have come north after working on Durham Cathedral. Money was raised for the construction by the sale of udal lands, and the first phase of the building was completed and consecrated in 1154.

In 1919, during extensive renovation, stones were found to be loose in one of the pillars. In the cavity revealed behind the stones lay a box containing a human skeleton. The damage to the skull corresponded with the details of the death blow inflicted on Magnus as told in the saga. A hundred years earlier another kist had been found containing bones now believed to be those of Earl Rognvald. Today the relics of both saints are sealed in caskets within the pillars which formerly flanked the high altar. The cathedral, which is in constant use, is considered to be one of the finest examples of Norman architecture in the country.

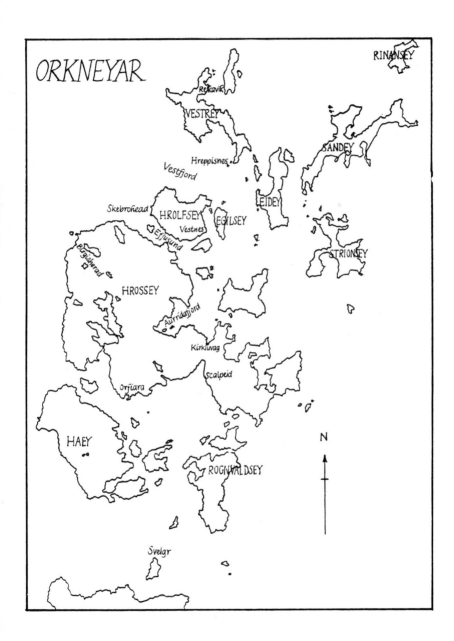

ORKNEYAR

RINANSEY

Reykavik

VESTREY

SANDEY

Hreppisnes

Vestfjord

EIDEY

Skebrohead

H.ROLFSEY

EGILSEY

Vestnes

Ejjusund

STRIONSEY

Eirgisherad

HROSSEY

Aurridafjord

Kirkuvag

Scalpeid

Orfiara

HAEY

N

ROGNVALDSEY

Svelgr

Murder the Foundation Stone

I

In the beginning
there was nothing,
neither sand, nor sea,
nor cooling surf.
There was no earth,
no upper heaven,
no blade of grass,
only the great void . . .

until Odin the all-father
lifted up land,
made middle earth
a matchless place.
Sun shone from the south
on a world of rock;
from the ground there grew
green fields . . .

until God created
heaven and earth.
And the spirit of God

moved upon the waters.
And God said,
"Let us make man in our image,
after our own likeness."
And it was so:
heaven mirrored on earth,
earth reflecting heaven
until the images
were fused, and mimic man
strove by making
to emulate his God.
Even destruction became
creation of a kind . . .

until in the darkness of space
particle moved against particle,
dust on dust,
in swirling bands
of circling matter,
forming suns
and moons and stars.

II

The morning shone bright
around them, like a jewel.
Molten gold spilled
from the rising sun,
gilding the glassy sea.
Magnus looked upon the islands,
clear and pure as new creation.
Oars dipped and rose;
drops, bloodied by the sun's

12

birth, drowned in the whirlpool
eddies of the blades' track.
Bloody choppings slopped
the shadowed gunwale.

No breath of wind
shivered the sea
or ruffled the heron,
silent sentinel
in the ebb.

From the calmness of the ocean
a wave, white crested,
rose like a shining axe.
Curling to its quivering
height, the water hung
before its flashing blade
crashed frothed fury
across Magnus' frail craft,
flung flecks in the
startled air.

"An omen of ill."

"Turn back."

"Turn back
before it is too late."

Drenched in the prow
in the blood red water
of the sound,
Earl Magnus shook his head.

"Row on. It is the will of God.
Easter, the time of sacrifice."

**They saw
eight ships cut clean
like knives through
the shining ocean;**
cleave the glassy waters
in search of prey.

"Haakon Paulsson comes
with four times the
promised ships and men.
He does not mean to talk."

The air hung thick
with murderous treachery.

"Let him come,
him and his men."

In the small stone church on Egilsey,
betrayed trysting place,
Magnus Erlendsson went down
upon his knees to bare his soul
before his Maker. All the long night.
Stars pricked the dark heart of heaven.

"Forgive me, Lord, for I have sinned."

Magnus did not cower
in offered sanctuary.

He rode to his Jerusalem
to face his foes.
In the early dawn, grey cold,
he slipped from the priests'
protection to the stone hard,
treacherous foreshore.

Stained by the guilt
of his intention,
Haakon Paulsson
could show no mercy.

"Lay down your standard, Ofeig.
Take up the axe."
But Ofeig, white and trembling,
backed away from the
horror of the act.

"No!" Slowly. "No!" In panic.
"NO!" A scream that echoed
through Efjusund.

"Lifolf! You are our butcher
and our cook. You are accustomed
to dealing with red meat.
Take up your axe
and let the deed be done."

And Lifolf, lowly servant,
wept before the rival earls,
reluctant to do as he was bid,
reluctant not to, bound in fear.

"Do not weep for this,"

said Magnus. "The fault
does not lie with you,
but with him who bids you,
Haakon Paulsson, murderer
and Earl of Orkneyar.
I forgive you freely.
Stand before me, I pray you,
and swing your axe like a man.
Hew a great wound in my skull
as befits an earl.
I would not be topped
like any common thief."

Trinity of the cross.
Head bowed.

"I commend my soul to heaven."

Downward flashing blade.
Life gone.

With that mighty axe swipe
Haakon Paulsson made a martyr.
In that bloody butchery
he made a murderer.
The image was transfixed.
Always martyr.
Always murderer.
Evil held within itself
the seeds of good,
good of evil.

Energy, unleashed

17

in cataclysmic force,
convulsed matter
in violent turmoil.
Red lava spewed
burning from the crater's mouth;
grey ash hung on the
mountain's sulphurous breath
until the molten mass
laid down deep foundations
of the earth, layer
on layer,
on layer.

III

A light like a flame
burned intercession to heaven.

Over foaming tide roost
and dusty track
pilgrims flocked
to Birgisherad,
to the grave
of Magnus,
martyr.

Blind Bergfinn Skatason
ferried crippled Sigurd and Thorbjorn
over misted spindrift
to Orkneyar.

The blind boatman
and his wayfarers
shuffled into Christ's kirk

and kept vigil
by the grave
of Magnus.

All the long night.

And in the morning,
when the sun rose beyond the headland,
Bergfinn saw it for the first time.
The light of heaven streamed into him.
Sigurd and Thorbjorn uncurled stiffened limbs
and grew straight and supple as summer saplings.

Granitic and schistose
basement rocks
compacted
into slabbed
sandstone
and flagstone
in the dawning
of the world.

IV

(i)

The moon, slanting through
Bishop William's windows,
lay in fragments
on the stone flagged floor.
Haakon, the murderer,
had made atonement
for his sin:
the lands of the first bishopric
sloped fertile to the sea.

19

"I give no cognisance
to false rumours
of supposed miracles
made manifest at
the grave of Magnus, here
in Birgisherad.
Such imaginings may
emanate from the Devil
to lead us into
false witness. Beware
lest you fall under the sway
of the Prince of Darkness,
foul Lucifer himself.

Molten
masses
moved,
folded,
cooled,
cracked
in hair fine
fault lines
in granite
beds.

(ii)

Haakon was dead.
Paul, his son, consulted,
not with his Bishop,
but with his thanes.
William gazed upon a
fitful sea.

20

Magnus had an heir, his nephew,
Rognvald, born to the Norwegian
Kol of Agder and Gunnhild.
To him Norway's king had granted
half the earldom of Orkneyar.
William drummed his fingers
on the window ledge.

The boiling waters of
the narrow channel frothed fury:
the tide was on the turn.

William waited.

Rock built
upon
rock
built upon
solid rock.

(iii)

Clouds lowered
on a tumultuous sea.
Spindrift smoked
on the snort of the gale.
In Hjaltland William fretted,
anxious to sail for Orkneyar.

On the pitching deck
the captain spoke:

"For a fair wind

21

exchange a vow.
Exhume the bones
of Magnus, blessed martyr.''

William pondered, troubled,
doubts circling like black curs.
Slowly he nodded his assent.
Straightway the wind
veered to the north, the storm
abated and the ship set sail,
skimming light hearted over
the whale's track to landfall.

Cross bedded sandstone,
red, pink, purple,
layer upon layer upon layer
in the deep dark core
of the isles.

And still William waited.

(iv)

Pine logs blazed fierce on the
hearth of Kol of Agder.
Smoke hanging in the rafters
smelled of summer forests.
Bishop William twirled his goblet.
Jewels from Byzantium flamed
with the leaping light of logs.
The gold chalice, intricately wrought,
lay heavy in his hand.
He sipped the beaded wine.

"I have a dream," said Kol,
watching the firelight flicker.
"To build a great minster
in the northern isles."

               "Indeed?"

"To replace the
humble kirk of Thorfinn
in Birgisherad."

               "You are
very confident of victory."

"Who would deny Earl Magnus'
heir? My son has rights that
cannot be gainsaid. Who in
Orkney does not weep for
Magnus, blessed martyr?"

"A new seat for the bishopric?"

A log sparked.

"There have been rumours,
even as far afield as this,
of miraculous happenings
at Magnus' grave."

Silence hung thick as smoke.

"My Lord Bishop,
Magnus has more power
dead than alive.
He is worth a dozen Pauls

to you now . . ."

        "A cathedral
reaching to the stars?"

"Glorifying God."

Meandering streams,
murmurous with suggestion,
strewed deposits of
sandstone grains
in shifting channels.

(v)

The sea sang on the rocks of Birgisherad;
fulmars swooped crying over tufted pinks.
A gusting breeze snatched
the church bell's clamour,
drowned it in cacophony of
sea song and bird call that held
the salt sprayed isle.

William was waiting still.

He raised a jewelled hand in blessing.
Light cracked jagged.
Darkness drowned the prelate
like a rising tide.
Trembling, he fell on the grave
of Magnus, blessed martyr.
Lying on the cold stone
he was tormented by the
tattered clanging of the bell
wrung from the tower
by the whining wind.

25

"Forgive me, Lord.
Be merciful,
I pray."

Tears fell like jewels.

"Let me see again
and I will vouch for blessed Magnus.
Work a miracle here this day
to show his holy power.
Restore my sight; make me whole again.
Forgive me, Lord, forgive me."

Light blazed over the grave of
Magnus the martyr, brighter
than the stars.

"Blessed Mary, Mother of God . . ."

A pin prick filtered
the clouded eyeballs.
Slowly William raised his head.

"May the Lord be praised!"

The clear light of heaven
streamed into him
and the world lay fresh
before him.

Remorseless ice sheets
scoured the contours
of the land,
smoothing rough
sandstone slabs.

V

Heavy clouds hung low over
a sighing sea. Grey drizzle
misted salt spun grass.
On St. Lucia's Day Bishop William
summoned the chief men of the isles.
Like cormorants upon a rock they stood,
black round the gaping
grave of Magnus. Creaking, the coffin
was prised from its damp resting place;
the lid was lifted. They looked
upon the murdered corpse,
mouldering in its earth damp tomb.

In hallowed water
William washed the rancid
bones. Like sea scoured
shells upon the shore, sucked
by a thousand tides, they shone
white and gleaming in the gathering haar.

Three times William held
the knuckle bone in holy fire.
Three times it was not consumed,
but shone like burnished gold
in the golden flame.
Then, at last, the bone
ran molten in a cruciform,
a simple golden cross
from the marrow of the martyr.

And silence fell upon the chapel.

In a hallowed shrine above the altar
of the Lord, the sacred bones were laid.
And William, Bishop of the Orkneys,
sanctified Magnus, erstwhile Earl.
Swelling clear above the murmuring
of the ceaseless waves,
sweet voices rose to heaven.

Stone
upon
stone
upon
stone.

VI

Gunni, the bondi, grunted in his sleep,
turned restless under the coarse
blanket. The glowing embers
on the longhouse hearth sighed soft.

"Wheesht, man; lie at peace."

In his dreams Magnus stood
before him. His voice was like
unfathomed ocean deeps:

"This tell to Bishop William.
Magnus wishes to go forth
from Birgisherad to Kirkiuvag
where Almighty God shall of His mercy
grant healing of diseases
to those who seek his cure

in righteousness and faith.
This dream shalt thou boldly tell.''

And Gunni was disquieted,
for even in Hreppisnes in Vestrey
it was known how Paul had set his face
against Magnus and his miracles.
So Gunni, anxious, kept silence.
But on the next night Magnus
came to him again and he was
very wroth.

            ''This your dream
must be told to Bishop and to Earl in
Birgisherad. Go thither with all speed.
If you refuse to do this thing,
it will turn out ill for you
in this world and the next.''

Unhappy Gunni fluttered like a
moth by the candle's flame.
He could save his life and lose his soul,
or save his soul and lose his life.
With a worm of dread
coiled about his heart,
he sailed for Birgisherad.
Before Bishop William
and Earl Paul and the worshippers
at Mass, halting,
he told his tale,
head bowed.

Immediately a great clamour broke out
of men urging Paul to remove the bones
to Kirkiuvag according to the words
of Magnus, saint and martyr.
The Earl turned as red as blood
and it was as if he had water in his mouth.

"It is a wise man," he said at last,
"who takes note of the turning of the tide."

In slow procession
William and his men of God
turned east to Kirkiuvag,
and blessed Magnus' bones
were borne towards the rising sun
to lie above the altar
in the grey walled town
beside the singing sea.

Swift braided rivers
fanned alluvial sandstone
in rippled layers,
grain upon red grit grain.

VII

Six war ships lay in the Hennoër
waiting for a wind.
Kol, Rognvald, Solmund, Harald,
Jon Fot and Aslak
laid claim to their swift keels
and chequered sails.

Green furrows, ploughed deep,
ran west to Hjaltland,
ridged by spumed sea rigs
smoking in the springtime gales.

"Many men," said Kol, the wise one,
"will be for Earl Paul,
the white tailed eagle,
against you, my son. Therefore
seek help where it is abundant.
Pray to Magnus, your uncle,
that he grant you the ancestral lands
that were his and are thine.

Make a vow

that, if you win your rightful realm,
you will build a church of stone
in Kirkiuvag, more magnificent than any
in the land. Let it be dedicated
to St. Magnus, the Earl, your kinsman.
Let his relics be consecrated there
and let it be the episcopal seat
of all the isles."

There, by the grey seaflux
of the Norwegian fjord,
Rognvald Kolsson
swore his oath.

And the wind set fair,
and they rolled their dragon prows
into the swelling waves.

Deep blue lagoons
and ice cold mountain
lakes held fast the
swirling grains
of fine ground stone
in thickening layers.

VIII

Sweyn, son of Asleif,
burst like a fireball
in northern skies.
A flaming meteor,
he blazed his course
through history.
The reddener of the
raven's claw,
accosted at Paul's Yuletide feast
with Sweyn Breastrope's taunt:

"Sweyn must be Sweyn's death,
and Sweyn shall be Sweyn's death,"

hacked down the carper, Breastrope,
in his cups. Spilled
his bright blood
amongst the wine
of Paul's drinking hall
in Orfiara.
The murder done,
under the paleness of a winter's moon,
he slipped silent through a window
slit and took horse across the wild
moors towards the sea at Aurridafjord

and thence by silent boat
to Egilsey and the sharp eye
of Bishop William
among his plump cushions.

"Breastrope was my father's foe.
Revenge will have revenge, Bishop.
Sword must answer sword."

"Sweyn Breastrope was
a loutish drunkard,
his death a good riddance.
But the old age is gone, my son.
Odin, Thor and Frey are dead.
The last battle has been fought
at Ragnarök. Our destiny
no longer is destruction
with chaos the only outcome.
You are born to a
new trinity of hope
whose redemptive love
will save your soul
and the world's."

"The old ways die hard, Father."

"The old ways, my son, have
a directness that commends them.
That hungry war hawk, Paul,
flies in the face of peace.
The old code would answer well for him."

The candle guttered
in a sudden draught.

"Grant me sanctuary, Father."

"I will see you safe,
Sweyn, son of Asleif.
While you remain here, an outlaw,
you are a danger to us both.
There is a swelling moon tonight.
A surf dragon leaves on the flood
for Tryvist and the western isles."

"I thank you, Father.
You can be sure that
your word wisdom
falls on fertile ground."

Igneous rock
pierces thicknesses
of overlying slabs
in vertical
intrusive dykes,
bubbling through
ancient sandstone
like liquid tar.

IX

Like Thor's hats,
beacons sat on every hill.
Leaping flames would warn Paul
of Rognvald Kolsson's coming.

In his northern lair
Kol crouched
like a forest fox.
Then, the wind set fair,

35

he slipped from Hjaltland
with six oar steeds.

"Back water
and hoist your sails.
We will confound at once
the laws of nature
and the watch on Fridarey."

The ships, rowed against
their sails, held steady.

Dagfinn, on Fridarey,
saw them swelling monstrous
on the grey horizon.

"The Norwegian comes!
Fire the beacon!"

Flames leaped skyward,
blazing brands of war.
Dagfinn took boat to join
his Earl in Orkneyar
while Kol, laughing, crept back
to Hjaltland's haven.

"Few men are so wise," he said,
"that they see everything there is."

"Mercy on us! Fridarey's alight!
Quick, Thorstein, fire the beacon!
Light your brand, man, plunge
it in the kindling's heart.
Rinansey must not be laggard
in her watch. They will not say

that Thorstein, Ragna's son,
was slow to his task.
Let the flames leap high
and let us pray that
those drunkards on Sandey
are awake to see them.
Quick, man! Quick!"

"Haad your wheesht, woman.
I'm coming."

From hill to hill raging fires
shrieked coming chaos.
Chiefs and bonder took to sea
with Paul their Earl to face
the bold usurper,
the sword bringer.
Three days and nights they waited
outside Kirkiuvag.
Three days and nights
the furtive fox
did not break cover.

"A false alarm.
You should not have
fired your beacon, Thorstein.
The mistake was yours."

"How so? Dagfinn's bonfire
was ablaze. Was I to know that he
could not tell a clutch
of fishing smacks from
the Norwegian fjord-elks?
He must bear the blame of it."

Dagfinn grew dark like a
smouldering storm cloud.
"More people have come to harm
by your hand than by mine."

"In God's name, hold
your tongue!" Thundering,
Thorstein swung his axe
and cut down Dagfinn of Fridarey.
For, he said, he had little
time to spare.

Then axes danced.
Sword metal pealed on
rim of shield.
Sigurd of Vestnes
and his son, Haakon Klo,
and Brynjulf and Hlödver,
Dagfinn's father; even
the Earl himself could
scarcely sunder them.
Until, at last, Kugi
of Vestrey spoke:

"The glittering serpent from
Norway's fjords
has set us at each other's throats.
Let him not succeed,
for the dark dragon
waits to fly again."

Stone built on stone
built on solid stone.

X

Resentment smouldered
among Paul's men
like the grey embers
of their burned out beacons.
Bitter ashes.

Meanwhile Kol, cunning fox
of the Norwegian forest,
sent Uni to Fridarey
to tend the new built beacon,
to watch the empty sea
for ships that never came . . .
to trickle water on the garnered
twigs and heather until the
driftwood pile was soaked,
a sodden mass.

Layer upon layer
upon layer
laid down in
the bedrock
of the world.

And Kol and Rognvald
lay in Hjaltland
and bode their time.
Tides rose and fell,
circling on the phases
of the moon.
Winds tossed mares' tails in the sky.

39

"We will wait for an easterly,"
said Kol, "for that will bear
us easily to Vestrey
and will confound
the salt waves' play
so that towering seas and
a head wind will hold
Paul fast in Hrossey."

At last, in spring sunshine,
the fleet of the otter's world
billowed buoyant
over plumed wave crest.

"Fire the beacon!"

But the dripping driftwood
lisped a despairing sigh,
hissing towards extinction.
No warlike flames leaped skyward
on Fridarey to warn
the southern isles.
Orkneyar slept
like a shoal of basking sharks
beneath the bright eyed sun.

Passage beds, flags,
sandstones, marls:
layer upon layer
in the deep foundation
of the isles.

Rognvald, the giver of rings,
made safe landfall
at Rekavik on Vestrey's shore.

In Helgi's feasting hall
bright flames leaped high
as fat dripped from the ox
roasting on the spit.
Dark haired maidens
served, swift as shadows.
Plucking on his lyre,
his spirits high,
Rognvald worked word music
as the ale horn passed
from lip to lip.

"Wave play and windfall bring
war steeds to Vestrey.
Bold warriors do battle in the name of
blessed Magnus, sainted martyr.
Brothers in bond friendship
bear arms with the ring giver.
Vestrey shall herald victory,
valiant deeds and vanquished foes!"

The bonder liked his style.
Even Kugi, Paul's man, pledged allegiance
to the warrior skald.

But Kol, sitting in the shadows
of the firestone's arch, cautioned:
"Praise no day until evening,
no sword till tested,
no ice till crossed,

no ale till drunk,
no maid till bedded,
no wife till buried.''

And one dark night secret
murmurings of betrayal
came to Rognvald's ears
and he surprised Kugi and his men
in the thickness of their plotting.

"Crooked irons clasp friend
Kugi's fetlocks and fetter him,
night wandering nomad,
nocturnal plotter. Pledges
made between men of honour
must be sacred, secret
meetings on the midnight ended.''

So Rognvald chid their
treachery in song
and pardoned them.

Amazed at his benevolence,
again the bonder pledged their troth.

XII

While Rognvald feasted,
warmed in the glow
of Helgi's hall,
Paul fretted, held fast
on Hrossey by the

cold east wind.
The white tailed eagle
took counsel with his men.

Some said fight;
some, buy the Norwegian
off with gold;
some, give Magnus' heir
his true inheritance.

Tossed in a roost of tides,
Paul swirled in uncertainties.

"Bitter is the wind tonight," he said,
"and white the tresses of the sea."

But Rognvald, calm in the assurance
of his vow, summoned William,
Bishop of the Orkneys,
to mediate between them.
And William, with a smooth tongue
and an oiled smile,
won fourteen days and nights of truce
towards the making of a proper peace.

And at last the wind changed airt
and Paul set sail for Hrolfsey
to speak with Sigurd
of how to trap
the raiding forest fox.

XIII

Thick dykes of rock
thrust through the
slabbed stone
of the foundation beds,
bursting from
the fiery molten
mass of middle
earth.

Through Efjusund an iron studded
dragon beat its wings like an
eagle of the high mountains.
Athwart its bows the flight scorning hero,
the battle tried one,
gazed again on Orkneyar.

"No man can banish
Sweyn, son of Asleif,
from these isles.
The reddener of the raven's
claw will not be tamed.
The old gods demand revenge.
They have their champions still!"

His beaked steed ran swift
before a south west wind
through a seething tide
towards Hrolfsey.

Men scrambled
like black beetles
below Skebrohead.

45

"Let us seek news.
Lie low upon the decks,
all except ten,
and leisurely proceed
as traders might."

Oars shipped,
the boat angled
landward, slow.

"Ahoy, there!
What news?"

"A truce between the earls.
Peace for twice se'en nights.
What's with you?"

"Fresh from Skotland
with goods for Paul."

"Make for Vestnes,
east along the coast.
Unload your cargo there
and Paul will feast you
in Sigurd's drinking hall
when he returns."

"When he returns?"

"He hunts otter here with us
since crimsoned dawn.
But our sport is nearly done
and we return to Vestnes
for ale and meat.
Sail on; we will meet you there!"

Sweyn Asleifsson, chuckling
from the deck boards,
steered his ship into a
hidden bay.

"We've got him now!"

Axe proud men slipped stealthy
from beached oar steed.
Reddeners of the wolf's jaws
crept towards the rock fast head,
lay low among the heather.
Below, hunters of the otter,
loud mouthed in loose laughter,
clambered careless up the rocky face.

Axes flashed fire, sword
metal pealed on rim of shield,
blood thirsty blades bit deep.
The Valkyries crossed
their broad loom
with a crimson weft.
Bodies lay on the cold grey
rocks like storm tossed wreckage.

Paul alone was left to live,
dragged like a stricken deer to
the snarling dragon prow.
East by Svelgr they held their course
to Atjöklar and Paul's half sister,
the Countess Margaret.
There was no comfort
in her black spider welcome
now she held Paul meshed
in her fine spun web.

Sigurd, searching for his laggard guests,
came upon the nineteen dead,
strewn like flotsam
on the shore.

Beside the hunted hunters lay
their sleek otters, rigid in
lip snarling death.
In the bright hard light of spring
the precious hoard of life
lay spilled, rubies of blood
jewelling the dew sharp grass.
Beside his own men, six strangers
lay stretched upon the shore,
plundered treasure chests.

Only Paul was missing,
spirited from Skebro
as by a sorcerer's spell,
and none lived who might
tell the tale.

Like a hive of bees
before a swarm,
Orkneyar buzzed.
Betrayal? Kidnap? Murder?
Treachery? Magic? Miracle?
Magnus? William? Rognvald?
Who? Why? How?
Where? When?

Molten lava frothed
from the crater's mouth
ridging in rivulets
down the grey ashed
mountainside.

XIV

So, quietly, Rognvald, the giver of rings,
assumed the earldom and was magnanimous.

"Magnus the martyr has cut the web of war.
God in His mercy has smashed the Valkyrie loom.
No warp is stretched of human entrails.
No dead men's heads hang as weavers' weights.
No blood wet spears make hoddle rods,
no spent arrows shuttles, no dripping swords
weave the web of battle.
The blood red cloud rolls from the sky.
Let the Valkyries lament their loss.
Let poetry take the place of battle
for the voice sings sweeter than the sword."

"Then put up your sword.
Grant amnesty
and I will tell a tale."

So, boldly, Sweyn Asleifsson showed himself
in grey walled Kirkiuvag
before Rognvald and his thanes.
Bishop William spoke for him,
and Rognvald, the peacemaker,
listened to his saga.
But the tale of Sweyn,

49

the raven reddener,
was not quite complete.

"There are times to speak,
and times to hold your tongue."

He left it to another time
and another place
and another teller
to unfold Margaret
of Atjöklar's fine spun plot:
that Harald, her son,
laid claim to half of Orkneyar,
his kidnapped uncle's share.
And, sworn to support him in that claim,
was Paul's kidnapper,
Sweyn, son of Asleif,
boldest manipulator of them all.

Sandstone, flag,
marl, dyke,
smooth, ridged,
laid down
in the foundations
of the earth.

Rognvald, grown in wisdom,
thought on the tragedy
of his uncle Magnus and Earl Haakon.
He thought on the strife
between himself and ill fated Paul.

"The sibyl prophesied that
brothers would battle to bloody end
and sisters' kin commit foul acts,
that there would be woe in the world,
wantonness rampant,
an axe age, a sword age,
when shields would be sundered,
a storm age, a wolf age
before the world crumbled.
No mercy or quarter
would man give to man.
The sun would grow dark,
earth sink in the sea,
the bright stars fall from the skies,
flames rage and fires leap high,
heaven itself be seared by heat.
The sibyl spoke of Fate,
remorseless destruction,
cataclysmic chaos,
the last battle at Ragnarök.

But that battle has been won
by Christ on Calvary. His suffering
has redeemed our souls. His love
purifies our spirits. Therefore in love
I embrace Harald as my foster son.
Together we will rule these isles in peace.

Now one thing alone remains:
my pledge to God, sworn
by the grey Norwegian fjord
in the springtime of my mission
when the issue stood uncertain.
Now, as Earl of Orkneyar,

I redeem that pledge.
I will build in Kirkiuvag,
here, by the whispering bay,
a mighty church of stone
for Magnus, saint and martyr.''

So events,
unclear in themselves,
laid together
block on block,
came at last
to form a whole.

XV

When summer sun
ruled the midnight sky,
Kol chose his site
and marked it out.
By the light drenched
whispering bay,
he dreamed his dream.

"As long as stone and mortar stand,
my son and I will stand immortal
beside Magnus, blessed martyr."

From the vast concourse of the
Viking world that stretched
from Iceland to Byzantium,
Kol culled ideas for his mighty work.

"All the skill and craftsmanship

of Europe and the East
will facet this jewel,
a ruby set in silver seas,
a gem blazoning purity of beauty
on all who see it."

The perfecting of that stone
laid bare his heart to heaven.

Turf stripped from the land,
earth laid bare.
Earth stripped from the land,
stone laid bare.
Stone laid on stone,
laid on stone.

From the bowels of the earth
they hewed the slabs,
dragged them from the dark groin
of the islands' depths,
fashioning the land they lived on
to the master mason's will.

XVI

Matthew, master mason,
smoothed the parchment
on his rough deal bench.

"That Kol of Agder has a dream!
Red stone stained by the dying sun,
red like a martyr's blood,
red like a full blown rose.
Martha, it will be magnificent!"

53

"You are a poet, Matthew."
She strewed sweet rushes
on the earthen floor.

"No. Rognvald
tools words.
Kol dreams dreams.
I grasp his dreams
and give them form."

"That is poetry too."

"They tell me, Martha,"—
he turned towards her,
hands like flames—
"that in the isle of Eidey
there is a sandstone
golden as ripening corn.
Imagine—
honeyed rock
on rose red flags
from Holland's Head.
Red on gold,
blood and corn,
a sacrifice in stone."
His face was bright
in the cruisie's glow.

Slowly she straightened,
hands on hips,
and her face was hard
like quarried stone.
"Sacrifice!
I am the only sacrifice
to your cold kirk.

Here, in an alien land,
among an alien people.''

"Listen to me, woman.''
He clasped her shoulders
in firm, warm hands.
"I have a vision of a minster
reaching for the stars.
Crafting that vision
will fulfil my life.
My soul aches to shape the stone,
to draw vaulted arches rooted
in the ground
towards heaven,
to raise heavy, earth bound
clay to dizzying heights,
to lift pillars and towers to hang
above this dwarfish town.
There is a need within me
to make real Kol of Agder's dream
and in that making
I will find myself.''

"In that making
you will glorify a cruel God—
a God that kills babbies!''
Her voice rasped dry and hard
as wind in autumn reeds.

"Hush, wife, that's past
and done with.''

His arm slid round her.
Her head hung
and her voice was low.

"That never will be done with."

"Think on the living, Martha—
Eleanor and William,
Richard and the twins.
Your life lies in them.
It is in creating
that we find our God;
in aspiring that we fine our spirits
towards purity.
I deal in stones and mortar,
you in mortal clay.
I perfect artefacts,
you shape genealogies.
What greater creation
can there be?
Live for the living, woman."

Her eyes tremored,
like sea pools
in a sudden gust.

"As long as we two live,
our babby lives.
The dead must never
be forgotten.

Nor the One
who let him die."

Bitter ashes.

XVII

Metal rang on rock,
clear as a tolling bell.
Hammers swung
rhythmic.
Slabs, prised from
earth's crust, fell free.
Caloused hands
chipped, chiselled,
chivvied, smoothed,
shaped, fondled,
caressed, curving
the grained slabs,
rose red and corn yellow.
Flower and fruit.

Among the dusty debris
Father John picked his way,
stooping under planked
scaffolds, side stepping rubble
and staved tubs of mortar.
Labourers, sweating, scaled
the rising walls
with loaded hods.
Masons laid block on block,
red on yellow,
yellow on red,
in startling polychrome.

Silent, with measured tread,
the prelate paced the site.
But in his heart
happiness carolled
uncontrolled.

"Praise be to God
for this great work,
here in sleepy Kirkiuvag.
Such an outburst of faith
unrivalled in our
northern hemisphere."

From the eye of the sun
a lark sang unseen.

"God moves in a mysterious way . . .
Glory be to God, the Immaculate
Master of Monks."

From half built piers,
solid at his feet,
he saw imagined pillars spring.
From ornate capitols
arches leaped
across the choir,
soaring skywards
in supplication.
Arcading vaulted the nave,
echoing the upward thrust,
drawing men's eyes
with the rising stone
ever upwards, to heaven.

"This church will be
a prayer in stone,
a symbol of man
reaching for his Maker.

58

O God, Lord and Father,
blessed be Thy name.
Purify our immortal souls
for everlasting life.
We are not worthy . . .''

XVIII

Huddled in the Viking houses
by the water's edge,
Helga wept.

Love's honeyed potion,
drunk deep,
turned to caustic poison
in the gut.

Jaundiced jealousy
sickened to
hard tongued grief.

Anger twisted
its burning knife.

"He called me his snow white lady
of the silver bracelet.
See how carefully he tooled
the glittering snake
and wound it round
my slender wrist.
Like the serpent coiled now
hard about my heart.

59

Thorfinn, the fickle maker
of fragile bracelets,
also forges swords of war.
He should have crafted
me a shining blade.
Look how he ogles
that black eyed hussy
from across the water,
that lascivious wanton,
the master mason's daughter."

Block
laid on
block
laid on
hard edged
block.

XIX

Sculpted in orange light and shadow
from the fierce glow of the goldsmith's
forge, Bishop William
smiled, benign, on Thorfinn.

"This bishopric of Orkneyar
is famed throughout the land.
Men dare the white maned
whale's track to seek a cure
at the shrine of Magnus,
blessed martyr. My cathedral
shines like a precious gem
in the church's crown.

No treasure is too rich
for such a see. I want
the best. Only the best."

"This is the best."

Thorfinn, the Viking,
held the gleaming cup
in flickering firelight.
His finger caressed
its golden tracery.

"Here, my Lord Bishop, are
the intertwining serpents of
Norse mythology,
here Odin, the all-father,
devoured by the fiery wolf—
the downfall of the pagan gods.
And on this side,"—
turning the goblet towards
the light—"on this side,
you, your Holiness,
with book and
cross, bruising, you see,
the serpent's head.
Pagan and Christian.
Fitting for a Norse cathedral."

Bishop William beamed,
mopping his brow
before the furnace heat.

"I commend your skill,
young man. There is
poetry in your artistry.

Such an artefact
offers immortality
for the sculpted
and for the sculptor.
Excellent, I say again,
excellent.''

William gone, Thorfinn
held the cup before him,
a smile upon his lips.
''You are right in that at least,
my Lord Bishop.
This is immortality.
The old gods, the new gods . . .
what are the gods
but man's creation?
The created creating his creator?''

Block
laid
on
block.

XX

''Checkmate.''

The chessmen glowed golden
in the candles' flame.
Rognvald laughed, sharp eyed.
Kol spread his hands
in resignation.

"I am glad to see your mind
maturing with your years."

"Life's a marvellous sharpener
of men's wits." Bishop William
spoke from the shadows
beyond the fire's glow.

"You must listen then," said Rognvald,
"to what I have to say.
Building must stop. You must
make an end while there
is yet money in my treasury."

"Never!" said Kol. "That kirk is
my life's work."

"Never!" said Bishop William.
"That kirk is my seat of power."

"Cut short your plans
or unfinished walls will crook
to heaven, an everlasting
symbol of a broken vow.
What will men say then?
We will be a laughing stock,
condemned from Greenland to the Ind
as breakers of our pledge,
unworthy of God's or Magnus' help."

"Our vow was made.
Our vow will be kept."

"But how, father?
Our coffers stand empty.
Our tide is ebbing fast."

63

"I trust the
infallible Helmsman
to steer my journeys."

"Sometimes He needs
a little help."

Bishop William snorted
like a rearing colt.
"Tax the people.
They can afford to pay."

"Not my people,"
said Rognvald.
"They would not
thank me for it."

"You are changed, my son.
With each turn of
the seasons' wheel
your green oats are
tipped with gold."

"The gold of wisdom," said
Earl Rognvald, "pays for nothing.
You must find coin
and find it fast."

XXI

A crescent moon hung like a horn
in the star bright sky.
Soft skin glowed creamy white,
sweet smelling on the banks of

Scalpeid. Dark hair, unbraided,
tumbled loose about her face, over
her swelling breasts. "Oh, Eleanor!"
It was a moan from the
deep core of his being,
primeval, wild.
Like a burnished god he glowed
bright and hard in the moonlight.
And she sighed, sobbing with the
waves that caressed the shore beneath
them where they lay. And it was all
starlight and seasong and the wind whispering
secrets on the midnight air.

Block
laid on
block
laid on
block.

XXII

Shadows licked the beams
of the great feasting hall,
quiet in the gathering dusk.
Rognvald threw off
his cloak and flung himself
on scattered furs.

"I will make a verse on this!"
he cried. "Don't you see?
It solves it neatly.
When a man dies,

his heir pays me,
his udal lord, in gold.
We get the money now,
and the land
becomes the man's forever."

"You give up your claim
upon the land."
Kol stroked his grey beard.

"In name only."

Bishop William's shining face
oozed a smile. "I commend
the Earl on his acuity.
There's money to be had there,
my lord, and plenty of it."

"Build on, Kol!
Create your dream!"

Between the turf roofed huts
clustered round the
quiet bay the minster
slowly rose, blood red
to heaven.

XXIII

Close by, in Olaf's kirk,
deep shadows gloomed.
Eleanor spoke quickly
like a running tide.

"Bless me, Father,
for I have sinned."

"In what have you sinned, my daughter?"
The quiet voice of Father John
soothed the grey stone.

"I cannot say!"

"Compose yourself, my child.
God the Father is merciful.
A sin of the flesh?"

"A mortal sin."

"Lustful thoughts, my child?"

"Would they were thoughts!"
(Murmured low
as the whispering sea.)

"Deeds, my child?"

"Love, father."

"The lynch pin
of Christendom."

"Unlawful love."

"In the name of the Father
and of the Son
and of the Holy Ghost . . ."

"I am with child."

Block
on
block.

XXIV

"By Mary's bones! A daughter of mine!
I will tear her limb from limb!"

"Calm yourself, Matthew.
She is but a child."

"And I expect the father is one
of these wild Vikings, eh?"

"A Norseman, yes. But
like yourself, an artist too."

"Well, he has created more than he
bargained for this time!"

Damp peat hissed
on the hot hearth.
Ash drifted white,
like snow.

"Think of the child, Matthew.
Think of the poor child.
A new babby." Her eyes glowed soft.

"They should have been wed first
like proper Christian folk."

"Remember—you said—
there is no greater creation . . ."

"Her soul will be damned to hell."

"She is no worse than Mary,
Mother of God. What was she
but an unwed mother,
betrothed to Joseph,
their son born an outcast
in a stable?"

"Silence, woman!
I will have no such talk
under this roof tree."

"But, Matthew, it's still
a babby, is it not?"

Flames licked blue
at the reluctant turf.
Her sweet words twined slow
about his heart.

XXV

From the grey walled town
blood red the minster rose,
uniting earth and heaven.
Solid in the centre
of the town it glowed,
all things to all men.

Like golden chessmen on a chequered board,
moving from light to dark, from dark to light,

70

until the game is lost and won,
they all had played their part:
Magnus, blessed martyr,
Haakon Paulsson, murderer,
Ofeig, standard bearer,
Lifolf, butcher,
blind Bergfinn Skatason,
Gunni of Vestrey, dreamer,
William the Old, Bishop of Orkneyar,
Kol of Agder, architect,
Rognvald, born Kali Kolsson,
earl, poet, gentleman,
Gunnvald, keeper of the light on Fridarey,
Uni, bold saboteur,
Sweyn, son of Asleif, wreaker of revenge,
Earl Paul, his victim,
Margaret of Atjöklar, cunning countess
and Harald, her son,
Matthew of Durham, master mason,
Martha, his wife, doubter,
Eleanor, their dark eyed daughter,
and her goldsmith, Thorfinn,
Helga, his slighted lover,
Father John, man of God, confessor,
and all those who loved, hated,
plotted, killed, quarried, carved
to create their work of art,
their testament.

The chequered squares fuse,
dark shadows licking on the white,
gold firelight flickering on the black.
In creation's fining flame
the chessmen shine a purer gold.

71

XXVI

In the springtime of the year
as the sun coursed higher
in the sky and tides
lipped at the full
before white spumed gales,
the bones of Magnus,
saint and martyr,
were borne from Olaf's kirk
beside the bay
towards the towering minster
at the heart of Kirkiuvag.
Magnus finally came home
to Magnus' kirk,
his circle done.

Rognvald, his cloak heavy
with golden thread,
lifted his hands to heaven:

"We thank God for a bloodless victory,
for the peaceful prosperity of
Orkneyar. We thank God for
the redemption of our pledge,
for this cathedral
raised to God's glory
in memory of our kinsman, Magnus,
blessed saint and martyr.

On this great occasion
I offer you a poem, for
wealth dies, kinsmen die,
a man himself must likewise die.

But word fame will never die
for him who works it well.

Red flared candle, flame
free to heaven in holy
intercession. Sweetly
scented rose of Orkneyar,
blushing, dusky bloom,
breathe incense skyward,
solemn sacrificial offering,
flame and flower, pure creation."

"We thank God," said Kol,
leaning on his staff,
"for this fulfilment of our lives.
For wealth dies, kinsmen die,
a man himself must likewise die,
but this church of stone will stand
as testament to the glory
of our times."

"We thank God," said Bishop William,
smilingly beneficent,
"for the endowment of this bishopric
in the earldom of Orkneyar. May Church
and State together glorify the name
of God the Father, Son and Holy Ghost.

Remember, wealth dies, kinsmen die,
a man himself must likewise die,
but one thing never dies:
the verdict on each man dead."

Voices swelled heavenwards,
resonant between the pillared
arches of the nave.

"We thank God for His grace
and mercy," said Father John.
"May His name be
forever praised."

XXVII

From evening's honeyed glow
Matthew led his wife
into the cool darkness
of the hallowed stone.

"I have made you immortal, Martha."

"You are not a God."

The quiet of the cathedral
closed about her, seeping
into her cracked soul.

"Here." Her eyes followed his,
upwards to the fretted frieze.
Familiar faces, carved above the pillars,
smiled down on her: the children—William,
Richard and the twins; Matthew
gazing love upon—herself.
In the welling silence
a star prick burned bright
about her heart.

He had made her beautiful;
carved soft roundness
from the rose red stone.
And next to her, Eleanor,
soft braided beside her
Viking, Thorfinn, and between them
their dimpling son.

"It is forbidden, Matthew!
They have sinned."

"And where are poor sinners
to come, but to the church of God?
In the apple of creation, Martha,
curls the worm.
From the tree of life
we pluck them both."

His arm enfolded her;
as one they stood
in the all-embracing sanctuary.
The spark glowing in her heart
burst into joyous flame.
The clear light of heaven
streamed into her
and the world lay fresh before her.

"Master mason," she breathed,
"you have truly made
a house of God."

Stone
on
stone.

PLACE NAMES

ATJÖKLAR	*Athole*
AURRIDAFJORD	*Bay of Firth*
BIRGISHERAD	*Birsay*
EFJUSUND	*Evie Sound*
EGILSEY	*Egilsay*
EIDEY	*Eday*
FRIDAREY	*Fair Isle*
HJALTLAND	*Shetland*
HREPPISNES	*Rapness*
HROLFSEY	*Rousay*
HROSSEY	*Mainland Orkney*
KIRKIUVAG	*Kirkwall*
LEIRVIK	*Lerwick*
ORFIARA	*Orphir*
ORKNEYAR	*Orkney*
RINANSEY	*North Ronaldsay*
SANDEY	*Sanday*
SCALPEID	*Scapa*
SVELGR	*Swelkie of Stroma*
TRYVIST	*Tiree*
VESTFJORD	*Westray Firth*
VESTNES	*Westness*
VESTREY	*Westray*

Elizabeth Hourston was born and brought up in Kirkwall. She was a pupil at Kirkwall Grammar School and subsequently attended Edinburgh University. She is married to an Orcadian and has two daughters. Her work has been published nationally in a variety of magazines and she was awarded the Poetry Society—Ceefax prize in 1982. A fun poem, "Kali Kolsson's Polychrome Cathedral" which tells the story of the events leading up to the founding of St. Magnus Cathedral, will be published in the spring of 1987.

Leila Thomson and Connie Hogarth are sisters. They were born and brought up in Hoxa, South Ronaldsay and both attended the Edinburgh College of Art where Leila specialised in tapestry and Connie in drawing and painting. After graduating, Leila visited the Faroes and Norway on a travelling scholarship before settling, like Connie, in Orkney.